Rocks & Minerals

Written by
Sandra Ford Grove and Dr. Judi Hechtman

Illustrator: Catherine Yuh

Editor: Karen P. Hall

Project Director: Carolea Williams

Table of Contents

Creative Teaching Press, Inc.

Introduction

The lessons in this resource are designed to provide you with all the information you need to offer meaningful, hands-on scientific explorations with minimal preparation and maximum results. Each lesson includes the following components.

Learning Outcome

At a glance, you can see how students benefit from the activity and the knowledge they will gain.

Process Skills

The process approach to science encourages divergent thinking and provides tools for students to learn about their world. The following process skills are highlighted in student explorations.

Investigating   Measuring
Predicting   Collecting Data
Experimenting   Recording Data
Observing   Inferring
Sorting   Communicating
Comparing   Constructing Models
Classifying

Connections

Additional activity ideas help students connect science concepts to other curriculum areas and to their own lives. This section includes a school connection to extend learning across the curriculum and a home connection to encourage family involvement.

Materials

A complete list of easy-to-find materials keeps preparation time to a minimum. You may wish to send home the parent letter (page 5) requesting help collecting materials.

Exploration

Each exploration has been designed to challenge and teach primary students through active participation. The teacher's role is that of facilitator—providing opportunities for scientific discoveries and encouraging students to raise questions. Questioning strategies are an important tool to extend student explorations and discoveries. Each lesson includes a few suggestions to help you get started.

Conclusion

This section includes background information and expected results. It may be presented before the exploration to guide instruction or after for more open-ended discovery.

Getting Started

Classroom environment is an important part of any science unit. Following are some suggestions for creating a stimulating environment that will motivate and excite students to explore science concepts. It is equally important to encourage family involvement as you begin your unit. Suggestions for making a home connection are also included below.

Exploration Station

Designate an area in the classroom for students to explore independently. Free exploration time will help students become familiar with the materials. You may wish to include:

- rock collections
- rock identification books
- various crystalline formations
- tools to test rocks (hammer, chisel, gloves, eye goggles, magnifying glasses)

Home-School Connections

Encourage family involvement and parent communication by sending home the parent letter (page 5) at the beginning of the unit. Encourage children to share classroom activities at home and invite parents to share in their child's learning experiences.

Learning Centers

Construct independent learning centers relating to rocks and minerals. Activities for learning centers may include a rock weigh station, rock polishing, rock and picture-card matching, rock sorting games, and pebble or sand art.

Bulletin Board

Dedicate a bulletin board in the classroom or hallway to science work. Display student diagrams, pictures, and writings from different explorations.

Literature Connections

Collect and display books about rocks and minerals. Use the bibliography (page 32) for book suggestions. Ask the school librarian or visit your local library for additional help. Prominently display the books in your classroom for easy access. Display poems about rocks and minerals on classroom walls.

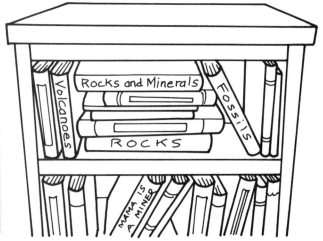

Creative Teaching Press, Inc.

Dear Family,

Our class is beginning an exciting science unit on rocks and minerals. We will be exploring and investigating differences between rocks and minerals, how rocks are formed, core sampling, weathering, mining, earthquakes, and much more. As part of this unit, students will have assignments to complete at home. Share in your child's excitement and offer assistance whenever needed.

Some of the explorations involve materials you may have at home. If you can send any of these materials to class with your child, we would greatly appreciate it.

- paper bags, plates, cups
- clear plastic cups
- food coloring
- colored sand
- colored cellophane
- gravel
- alum
- aluminum pie tins
- small shells
- 8-oz. milk cartons
- egg cartons
- film canisters
- 1-lb. coffee cans with lids
- clear plastic jars with lids
- marbles
- miniature marshmallows
- toothpicks

We welcome guest speakers on subjects relating to rocks and minerals. We would like to hear about topics such as rock collecting, earthquakes, volcanoes, gem formation, and core sampling. If you, or anyone you know, would like to speak to our class, please contact me.

Our study of rocks and minerals will be fun and exciting for everyone. Thank you in advance for being a part of your child's learning experience.

Sincerely,

Going on a Rock Hunt

Learning Outcome

Students learn to describe rocks using different physical attributes.

Process Skills

▶ Students **compare** rocks.

▶ Students **classify** rocks according to different physical characteristics.

▶ Students **communicate** their results through writing and discussion.

Connections

★ School

Have students create their own "rock concerts," using rocks, craft items, and shoe boxes to create the concert stage. Invite students to make other creations such as rock museums or rock animals.

★ Home

Invite students and their families to assemble rock collections, using shoe boxes and rocks from their neighborhoods. Have them group and classify rocks by size, color, or texture.

Exploration

In advance, prepare dirt sifters by using a pencil to poke holes in the bottoms of paper cups. Tell students they are to find and compare rocks collected around school. Distribute paper bags and invite students to label them (e.g., *Joshua's Rock Collection*). Have students collect rocks using sifters or their hands, then clean them in water tubs. Return to class and ask partners to compare rocks. Have them sort and classify by color, size, and texture. Ask students to mark six to eight rocks using different-colored crayons. Distribute magnifying glasses and lab sheets, and have students record their observations.

● How are your rocks similar to your partner's? How are they different?

● Which rocks are smooth? rough? dark-colored? light-colored?

● Besides color, size, and texture, what are other ways to describe your rocks?

Materials

- [ ] paper cups
- [ ] pencil
- [ ] paper bags
- [ ] tubs of water
- [ ] paper towels
- [ ] crayons
- [ ] magnifying glasses
- [ ] lab sheet (page 7)

Conclusion

Rocks are natural, solid materials that make up the earth. Students discover that rocks differ in size, color, and texture. Most rocks consist of inorganic substances, though some contain organic waste (shells, fossils). Geologists identify and classify rocks by texture, color, density (mass per unit volume), hardness, luster, magnetism, and cleavage (how they break). Extend learning by having students use balance scales to compare and sort rocks by weight.

Going on a Rock Hunt

Color the boxes to match your marked rocks. Check words that describe each rock.

Rocks	Smooth	Rough	Flat	Round	Dark-colored	Light-colored	Large	Small
☐								
☐								
☐								
☐								
☐								
☐								
☐								
☐								

What other words can you use to describe your rocks?

_____

_____

Which rock is smallest? largest? roundest? flattest? Color the boxes to match your choices.

☐ smallest   ☐ largest   ☐ roundest   ☐ flattest

What do you see looking at rocks through a magnifying glass? Write your observations below.

_____

_____

_____

Inside the Earth

Learning Outcome

Students learn that rocks are formed by the earth's layers.

Process Skills

▶ Students **construct models** to **investigate** rocks formed beneath the surface of the earth.

▶ Students **collect** and **compare** "core rock" samples from earth models.

▶ Students **infer** how rocks form from the earth's layers.

Connections

★ **School**

Read aloud *The Magic School Bus Inside the Earth* by Joanna Cole. Invite students to imagine traveling to the center of the earth. Have them write stories describing what they see, hear, and feel on their journeys. For extra fun, play mood music as students write and share their stories.

★ **Home**

Invite students and their families to create ice-cream models of the earth, scooping together different flavors to create the inner core and the mantle, then dipping into self-hardening chocolate to create the crust.

Exploration

Make multicolored cupcakes in advance—divide vanilla cake batter into three bowls, add different food colorings, spoon alternating layers of batter into muffin cups, and bake. Use a globe to highlight key features of the earth to students, explaining that three layers of rock lie underneath the earth's crust. Distribute Earth models (cupcakes) to students and have them use straws to extract "rocks." Ask students to poke straws deep into their cupcakes, then pull them out while covering the tops with their thumbs. Have students carefully blow through the straws to release their rock samples on napkins.

● How are your "rocks" similar? different?
● Do all rocks on Earth look the same? Why or why not?
● How did you extract your "rocks" from the cupcake? How do you think rocks from the center of the earth get to the surface?

Materials

☐ vanilla cupcake ingredients
☐ cooking utensils (mixing bowls, mixing spoons, muffin cups, cupcake tin)
☐ food coloring
☐ globe
☐ straws
☐ napkins

Conclusion

There are three major layers of rock under the earth's crust (surface)—the mantle, the outer core, and the inner core. Students simulate the way geologists extract rocks from the earth's layers (core sampling). Rocks may differ in composition depending on the earth layer from which they are extracted. Extend learning by inviting students to create models of the earth using foam balls and layers of colored clay.

Creative Teaching Press, Inc.

A Closer Look at Rocks

Learning Outcome

Students learn that rocks are composed of minerals.

Process Skills

▶ Students **observe** and **compare** assorted minerals and rocks.

▶ Students **construct models** to show that rocks are composed of minerals.

▶ Students **communicate** their results through artwork and discussion.

Connections

★ School

Display and discuss past and present artwork and jewelry made from rocks and minerals. Invite students to use colored gravel and glue to create their own mosaic pictures.

★ Home

Invite students to draw pictures that demonstrate to family members how minerals combine to form rocks. Have them color "rocks" by using a blend of four different colors, then ask family members to identify the "minerals" (colored crayons) used.

Exploration

Display rocks and minerals for students to examine and compare. Discuss how rocks are composed of minerals—natural, nonliving substances found on or in the ground. Explain that some rocks contain a blend of minerals that are difficult to distinguish. Give each student construction paper, cups of colored sand, cellophane, scissors, and glue. Invite students to draw rock outlines on construction paper and fill them to make two different "rocks"—one filled with blended sand and the other with overlapping cellophane pieces. Invite students to compare their "rocks."

● Is it easy or difficult to distinguish different colors in your rocks? Why or why not?
● What do you see when cellophane colors overlap in your "rock"?
● Why is it sometimes difficult to identify minerals that blend together in rock?

Materials

- ☐ assorted rocks and minerals
- ☐ white construction paper
- ☐ cups of colored sand (red, orange, yellow, blue)
- ☐ colored cellophane (red, orange, yellow, blue)
- ☐ scissors
- ☐ glue
- ☐ crayons

Conclusion

Some rocks contain only one mineral, but most are mixtures of two or more. Students discover that colors of sand or cellophane are difficult to distinguish when blended together in their rock models. This is similar to what occurs in real rocks—minerals may not always be distinguishable because they blend together. Extend learning by investigating the mineral compositions in real rocks.

Crystal Creations

Learning Outcome

Students investigate crystalline minerals.

Process Skills

▶ Students **experiment** with salt, sugar, and alum to create crystals.

▶ Students **observe** and **compare** crystalline structures using magnifying glasses.

▶ Students **record** and **communicate** their findings through writing and pictures.

Connections

★ School

Explore the water cycle and discuss how evaporation plays a part in the formation of crystals. Have students draw pictures to show that water evaporates from a solution to leave behind solid materials.

★ Home

Invite students and their families to make colorful rock candy. Have an adult family member supersaturate boiling water with raw sugar and pour the cooled solution into a jar. Invite students to add food coloring, insert a wooden skewer, and watch the sugar crystals grow over several days.

Exploration

In advance, cover work areas with newspaper. Label cups *Salt, Sugar,* and *Alum,* then fill ¼ full with corresponding solids. Explain to students that many minerals are made of crystals—solid structures (atoms) arranged in orderly, regular patterns. Divide the class into partners and give each pair three lids, a set of solids, a spoon, and warm water. Ask students to fill cups half-full with water and stir to dissolve solids. A small portion will settle to the cup bottoms and not dissolve. Have them label lids to correspond with the solids, then use eyedroppers to apply a thin layer of each saturated solution to the appropriate lids. Let lids sit overnight, then ask students to observe them with magnifying glasses. Have students record their findings in science journals.

● What happened to the solutions in the lids? Why?
● How are salt, sugar, and alum crystals similar? different?
● How do your crystals compare to the original samples?

Materials

☐ newspaper
☐ paper cups
☐ labels
☐ solids (salt, sugar, alum)
☐ jar lids lined with black construction paper
☐ plastic spoons
☐ warm water
☐ eyedroppers
☐ magnifying glasses
☐ science journals

Conclusion

Students discover cubic crystals when water evaporates out of salt, sugar, and alum solutions. Extend learning by having students examine other crystalline patterns in a "crystal garden" (teacher demonstration only). Mix 10 mL of water, 10 mL laundry bluing, 5 mL ammonia, 70 grams salt, and 2 drops food coloring. Spoon over a dry sponge, let crystals grow for 24 hours, and observe the results.

Rock Formations

Learning Outcome

Students learn how igneous, sedimentary, and metamorphic rocks are formed.

Process Skills

► Students **construct models** of igneous, sedimentary, and metamorphic rocks.

► Students **compare** rock models.

► Students **infer** how igneous, sedimentary, and metamorphic rocks are formed.

Connections

★ *School*

Read aloud *Volcanoes* by Norman Barrett. Invite students to research and report on volcanoes from around the world.

★ *Home*

Invite students and their families to construct model volcanoes using a clay base, baking soda, vinegar, and red food coloring. Have them place baking soda in the center of a clay volcano, add vinegar that has been colored red, and observe the "lava" bubbling out.

Exploration

In advance, tape paper cones to glue bottles, and place food items in separate bowls (one set for every three to four students). Discuss the three types of rock in the earth's crust— igneous, sedimentary, and metamorphic. Invite students to explore and compare rocks labeled *Igneous, Sedimentary,* and *Metamorphic.* Have students complete three different explorations to simulate the formation of these rocks.

Materials

- ☐ construction paper (brown, black)
- ☐ tape
- ☐ glue bottles
- ☐ "rocks" (mini marshmallows, cereal, nuts, chocolate chips, candy sprinkles)
- ☐ paper bowls
- ☐ pre-labeled igneous, sedimentary, and metamorphic rocks (volcanic rock, sandstone, marble)
- ☐ plastic zipper bags
- ☐ cooking utensils (pan, wooden spoon, hot plate or microwave)
- ☐ waxed paper

To simulate the formation of igneous rocks, have students squeeze "volcanoes" (cone-covered glue bottles) to push "lava" (glue) out of the top. Invite students to create glue "rocks" and let them harden on black construction paper.

To simulate the formation of sedimentary rocks, ask students to place "rock pieces" (food items) inside plastic bags and squeeze until pieces stick together. Have each student roll half of his or her mixture into a ball to create "sedimentary rocks."

Rock Formations

To simulate the formation of metamorphic rocks, ask students to place remaining sedimentation mixtures into a cooking pan (with adult supervision), and observe what happens when heated. Spoon melted "rock" onto waxed paper, let solidify, and give one to each student.

Have students compare their "rocks" and record their findings in science journals. Ask students to describe each rock and compare how the rocks were formed.

- How is the formation of your glue "rock" similar to the formation of igneous rock?
- How did you get the food items to stick together and form a ball? How do you think rock chips stick together to form sedimentary rocks?
- How is your sedimentary rock similar to your metamorphic rock? How is it different?

Conclusion

Students discover how heat and pressure contribute to the formation of rocks. Igneous rocks form at high temperatures when melted rock cools underground (magma) or erupts out of volcanoes (lava). Sedimentary rocks are formed when layers of smaller rocks, minerals, and fossils compress together. Metamorphic rocks are created when igneous and sedimentary rocks are altered by pressure, heat, or both. Extend learning by having students draw pictures in their science journals showing how igneous, sedimentary, and metamorphic rocks are formed.

Creative Teaching Press, Inc.

Layer by Layer

Learning Outcome

Students discover that sedimentary rock forms in layers.

Process Skills

▶ Students **construct models** of sedimentary rock.

▶ Students **observe** the layering effect of sedimentary rock.

▶ Students **communicate** their findings through pictures and discussion.

Connections

★ **School**

Explore shells and other fossils found in sedimentary rocks. Invite students to write imaginative stories about the formation of a sedimentary rock.

★ **Home**

Invite students and their families to make "sedimentary" sandwiches by layering food items between two slices of bread, then compressing pieces together.

Exploration

In advance, cover work areas with newspaper. Place sand, gravel, and shells in separate bowls, one set for every four students. Prepare Plaster of Paris and pour into empty milk cartons. Discuss with students how sedimentary rocks are formed, and display examples for students to examine. Distribute bowls of materials to small groups of students. Give each group member a carton of Plaster of Paris and a cup. Have students construct models of sedimentary rocks inside their cups by alternating layers of dry materials and Plaster of Paris. Allow "rocks" to harden overnight, then have students cut away the cups. Invite students to draw pictures of their rocks in science journals and share their results.

● Which materials in your sedimentary rock are visible? Which are hidden?
● How are sedimentary rocks similar? different?
● How do shells become part of sedimentary rocks?

Materials

- ☐ newspaper
- ☐ colored sand
- ☐ fine blue aquarium gravel
- ☐ large gravel or pebbles
- ☐ shells or "fossils" (beads, seeds, paper clips)
- ☐ paper bowls
- ☐ Plaster of Paris
- ☐ 8-oz. milk cartons, tops cut off
- ☐ sedimentary rocks (shale, sandstone, limestone)
- ☐ clear plastic cups
- ☐ scissors
- ☐ science journals

Conclusion

The creation of model "rocks" simulates how sedimentary rocks form—layers of sediment (rock pieces, minerals, shells, fossils) compress and adhere with natural cement (limestone). Extend learning by inviting partners to trade rocks, crack them open, and identify the components.

Settle Down

Learning Outcome

Students learn how sedimentary rock forms in riverbeds.

Process Skills

► Students **construct models** of riverbeds.

► Students **observe** and **compare** sediment layers.

► Students **communicate** their results through writing, drawings, and discussion.

Connections

★ School

Investigate what happens to litter and other man-made waste discarded in riverbeds. Discuss how water pollution affects rock formation as well as plants and animals living in riverbeds.

★ Home

Invite students and their families to visit rivers, lakes, streams, and oceans to explore and discover sedimentary rocks. Have them bring samples to school to share with classmates.

Exploration

Display sedimentary rocks for students to observe and compare. Explain that some sedimentary rocks form when layers of rock pieces and fossils settle to the bottom of riverbeds. Distribute jars and cups of sediments to each pair of students. Have partners add equal amounts of each item to the jar, fill with water, and place lids on tightly. Ask students to shake jars thoroughly, then set them on the table and observe what happens for five minutes. Have students draw and explain their results in science journals.

● What happens to materials immediately after you shake the jar? After five minutes?
● Which items settle to the bottom of the jar first? Why?
● How is the layering inside your jar similar to sedimentary rock forming in riverbeds?

Materials

☐ sedimentary rocks (sandstone, shale, limestone, fossiliferous sandstone)
☐ large plastic jars with lids
☐ cups of "sediment" (sand, soil, shells, gravel)
☐ water
☐ science journals

Conclusion

Students discover that materials in the jar settle in layers—the heaviest (gravel) sinks to the bottom first, followed by lighter materials. Over time, some smaller particles fall through the cracks, forming layers beneath and between larger pebbles. This simulates how sedimentary rock forms in rivers and other bodies of water—pieces of eroded rocks, minerals, and fossils settle to the bottom where they compress and adhere together. Extend learning by discussing weight and density. Invite students to add other items to their jars (leaves, seeds, branches), predicting where items will settle.

Creative Teaching Press, Inc.

Fossil Findings

Learning Outcome

Students discover how fossils are imprinted and encased in rock.

Process Skills

▶ Students **investigate** ways fossils are formed in rock.

▶ Students **construct models** of fossil imprints and castings.

▶ Students **infer** how scientists learn about dinosaurs and other prehistoric organisms.

Connections

★ School

Have students research fossil pictures of dinosaurs and other prehistoric animals at their school library or by using computer technology. Invite students to share their findings with classmates.

★ Home

Invite students and their families to explore and discover fossil remains at local museums. Have them compare and contrast imprints and molds of prehistoric organisms from different time periods.

Exploration

In advance, cover work areas with newspaper. Fill milk cartons half-full with sand. Prepare Plaster of Paris in a large milk carton just prior to beginning the exploration. Discuss with students how plant and animal parts form fossils in sedimentary rock. Have students perform three different fossil imprint activities.

First, give each student clay to mold into rock form. Have him or her make "fossil imprints" by pressing hard objects into their clay rocks.

Second, distribute sand cartons and ask students to use hard objects to make imprints in the sand. Give them cups half-full of Plaster of Paris to pour on top of their sand imprints, and let dry overnight. The next day, have students tear away the cartons to examine their "fossil molds."

Materials

☐ newspaper
☐ 8-oz. milk cartons, tops cut off
☐ damp sand
☐ Plaster of Paris
☐ large milk carton
☐ clay
☐ hard objects (shells, chicken bones, twigs)
☐ paper cups
☐ carbon imprinting items (leaves, wooden blocks, carbon paper, white paper)

Fossil Findings

Third, explain differences between carbon imprints and fossil molds. Divide the class into partners and give each pair a leaf, a wooden block, carbon paper, and white paper. Ask students to place leaves (veins facing down) on top of carbon paper (carbon side up), then cover leaves with white paper and rub with blocks to make carbon imprints. Have students compare their carbon imprints and "fossil" castings. Invite students to share their results with classmates.

- What are fossils? What kind of rock contains fossils or fossil imprints—igneous, sedimentary, or metamorphic?
- How does your carbon imprint compare to your fossil mold? How are they similar? different?
- Why are fossils important for learning about dinosaurs and other prehistoric animals?

Conclusion

Students discover that carbon imprints create outlines of solid objects, whereas fossil molds create 3-D impressions. Carbon imprints occur when carbon in decaying tissues forms a thin, black outline of the dead organism. Fossil impressions form when buried materials such as shells and bones dissolve. The hollow space left behind fills with mineral deposits, leaving a cast imprint. Extend learning by soaking sedimentary rock in an open jar of vinegar to dissolve limestone, then examine the fossils that are released. Note: Apply clear nail polish to exposed fossils and let dry before soaking rocks in vinegar. Rinse the released fossils with water before examining.

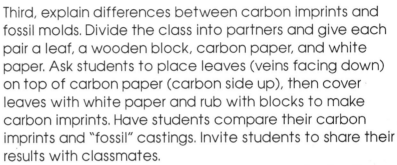

Plaster of Paris

16

Hard as a Rock

Learning Outcome

Students learn how to test for variations in the hardness of rocks.

Process Skills

▶ Students **measure** and **compare** the hardness of rocks using scratch tests.

▶ Students **collect** and **record data** from the scratch tests.

▶ Students **compare** and **classify** rocks according to test results.

Connections

★ **School**
Investigate how hard rocks and minerals such as flint and granite have been used to make tools throughout history. Invite students to compare and contrast tools from different time periods. For extra fun, have students design their own rock tools.

★ **Home**
Invite students and their parents to test and compare the hardness of rocks found in their neighborhoods. Have them sequence rocks from softest to hardest by rubbing rocks together and observing scratch marks.

Exploration

Ask each student to collect six rocks from around school and mark them with different-colored crayons. Have students use these colors to identify their rocks on lab sheets. Distribute rock salt to add to student collections. Explain to students that scientists identify and classify rocks by hardness. Ask students to scratch rocks with nails, pennies, and their fingernails. Have students observe and record on lab sheets which items leave scratch marks. Explain that soft rocks will be scratched more easily than hard rocks. Invite students to share and compare results.
● Which rocks had scratch marks from your fingernail? a penny? a nail?
● Which rock is softest? hardest? How do you know?
● Would soft or hard rocks be best for making tools? Why?
Caution: Supervise use of nails, instructing students to scratch rocks away from their bodies.

Materials
- ☐ rocks
- ☐ crayons
- ☐ lab sheet (page 18)
- ☐ rock salt
- ☐ pennies
- ☐ nails

Conclusion

Students discover that softer rocks, such as rock salt, scratch more easily than harder rocks. Scientists classify the hardness of rocks and minerals using a scale of one to ten (the Mohs scale), with one being the softest. Rocks and minerals scratched with a steel file (nail), but not with pennies or fingernails rank 7.5, those marked by both files and pennies rank 3.5, and those scratched by all three objects rank 2.5. Extend learning by having partners rub rocks together to compare and sort by hardness—harder rocks leave scratch marks on softer ones.

Hard as a Rock

Color the boxes to match your marked rocks. Check which items leave scratch marks on each rock.

Rock Samples	Fingernail	Penny	Nail
Rock ☐			
Rock ☐			
Rock ☐			
Rock ☐			
Rock ☐			
Rock ☐			

How many rocks had scratch marks from your fingernail? _____

How many rocks had scratch marks from the penny? _____

How many rocks had scratch marks from the nail? _____

I know that rock ☐ is the hardest because _____

_____

I know that rock ☐ is the softest because _____

_____

A Streak of Color

Learning Outcome

Students learn that rocks and minerals can be identified by streak colors.

Process Skills

► Students **predict** streak colors of rocks and minerals.

► Students **observe** and **compare** streak colors.

► Students **communicate** their results through writing and drawing.

Connections

★ School

Invite students to write a story similar to *The Ugly Duckling* featuring a rock. Have them describe a plain rock creating beautiful colors of the rainbow. Invite students to illustrate and share their stories.

★ Home

Invite students and their families to create streak-color pictures on unglazed white tiles. Have students share their creations with classmates.

Exploration

Invite students to bring rocks from home or select rocks from a class rock collection. Have them use labels to number six to eight different rocks. Ask students to record rock numbers and general appearance in their science journals. Explain that scientists determine the "true" color of rocks and minerals by performing streak tests. Demonstrate a streak test for students, scraping a rock on the unglazed bottom of a tile. Ask students to predict in science journals what color streaks their rocks will leave behind. Have them scrape rocks on tiles, then draw pictures of their results in science journals.

● What colors do you see in your rock streaks?
● Does the outward color of each rock match the color streak? Which do? Which do not?
● How could you prove that you and a friend have the same kind of mineral if the samples look different?

Materials
- [ ] assorted rocks
- [ ] labels
- [ ] science journals
- [ ] white tiles (unglazed bottoms)
- [ ] crayons

Conclusion

Students discover that most rocks and minerals leave distinct color streaks that may or may not be the same color as the rock itself. Scientists use streak tests to group and classify different minerals. Mineral "families" such as hematite and tourmaline may appear different on the outside, but all members leave the same streak colors. Extend learning by inviting students to create a color chart that includes pictures of rock samples and corresponding streak colors.

Bubbling Stones

Learning Outcome

Students learn to identify rocks containing calcium carbonate (limestone).

Process Skills

▶ Students **investigate** and test for the presence of calcium carbonate in rocks.

▶ Students **observe** that rocks with calcium carbonate bubble when exposed to vinegar.

▶ Students **sort** and **classify** rocks according to the presence of calcium carbonate.

Connections

★ School

Investigate different limestone building materials (cement, brick, marble). Invite students to use rocks and clay to build their own structures.

★ Home

Invite students and their families to investigate how many items in and around their homes contain lime or limestone, such as cement, marble, and toothpaste. Have students list items to share with classmates.

Exploration

In advance, cover work areas with newspaper. Invite students to choose six to eight rocks from a class collection or bring rocks from home. Explain that many rocks contain calcium carbonate—a natural cement that holds rock pieces together. Discuss how natural and man-made acids dissolve calcium carbonate in rocks. Distribute limestone, eyedroppers, and vinegar to each student. Ask students to place drops of vinegar (a weak acid) on limestone and observe the fizzing that indicates the presence of calcium carbonate. Have students place drops of vinegar on assorted rocks—those containing calcium carbonate will fizz and bubble. Ask students to sort rocks according to the presence of calcium carbonate, then share their results with classmates.

● Does limestone contain calcium carbonate? How do you know?

● How many of your rocks contain calcium carbonate? How many do not?

● What would happen to limestone if it is soaked in vinegar over long periods of time? Why?

Materials
- [ ] newspaper
- [ ] assorted rocks
- [ ] limestone
- [ ] eyedroppers
- [ ] cups of vinegar

Conclusion

Calcium carbonate is the main component of limestone, marble, coral, calcite, and chalk. Students observe that rocks containing calcium carbonate fizz and bubble when they come in contact with vinegar, a weak acid. Calcium carbonate dissolves and rock pieces fall apart when exposed to acid for long periods of time. Extend learning by inviting students to observe changes in rocks left in vinegar jars over several weeks.

Creative Teaching Press, Inc.

Rock Sort Games

Learning Outcome

Students combine concepts learned in prior lessons to identify and classify rocks.

Process Skills

▶ Students **sort** and **classify** rocks by physical attributes.

▶ Students **observe** and identify attributes used to sort rocks.

▶ Students **communicate** their findings to partners.

Connections

★ School

Have students cut and paste pictures of rocks and minerals onto 3" x 5" index cards. Invite students to invent games with their picture cards, such as "Rock Concentration" (students match identical rock pictures) and "Rock Rummy" (students group rock pictures by a common attribute).

★ Home

Invite students to create a "common attribute" poster, sorting pictures of rocks and minerals by common attributes and gluing them onto poster board. Ask students to include descriptive sentences underneath each picture group.

Exploration

In advance, use labels to number several rocks. Brainstorm with students ways to describe and identify rocks. Have students sit in a circle and place numbered rocks in the center. Play "I'm Thinking of a Rock" by giving students clues and having them identify the rock being described. Invite volunteers to give clues to identify a mystery rock.

Divide the class into partners and distribute twelve rocks, yarn, and egg cartons to each pair. Invite students to play the following sorting games.

● Ask a student from each pair to use a physical attribute (color, size, shape, texture) to secretly sort rocks into yarn circles. Have partners identify the attribute by which rocks were sorted. Ask students to switch roles and play again, sorting by another physical attribute. Challenge students to sort rocks by more than one attribute.

● Ask partners to select six rocks that vary in size and texture. Ask a student from each pair to close his or her eyes and feel a rock that partners have secretly selected. Have partners place rocks back into the collection. Ask students to open their eyes and identify the rocks they felt. Invite partners to choose new rocks and play again.

Materials
- ☐ labels
- ☐ assorted rocks
- ☐ yarn
- ☐ balance scales
- ☐ egg cartons

Rock Sort Games

- Distribute balance scales to pairs of students. Have them place a large rock on one side of the scale, then guess and test which combination of rocks to place on the other side to balance the scale.

- Have the class sit with partners in a large circle while sorting rocks (smallest to largest, smoothest to roughest, lightest to darkest) into egg cartons. Have each pair rotate to their right and identify the attribute used to sort the rock collection next to them. When the sorting method has been determined, ask partners to rearrange rocks using other attributes, then rotate again to their right when the signal is given. Have students continue to rotate, identify, and re-sort rocks until partners return to their original spots. Invite students to discuss and share different sorting methods.

Conclusion

Students discover that rocks may be grouped and identified by many different attributes, including size, weight, color, and texture. Extend learning by inviting students to sort rocks by type (igneous, sedimentary, metamorphic), hardness, streak colors, luster, and magnetism.

Tites and Mites

Learning Outcome

Students learn how stalagmites and stalactites form in caves.

Process Skills

► Students **construct models** of stalagmites and stalactites.

► Students **observe** the formation of simulated stalagmites and stalactites.

► Students **communicate** their findings through writing and drawing.

Connections

★ *School*

Invite students to create their own "caves" using large appliance boxes and construction paper stalactites and stalagmites.

★ *Home*

Have students and their families write imaginative stories about cave adventures. Invite students to share their stories with classmates.

Exploration

In advance, cover work areas with newspaper. Review crystallization with students, and explain how calcium carbonate (limestone) crystallizes to form stalagmites and stalactites in caves. Divide the class into partners and give each pair two cups of salt, a cardboard piece, spoon, yarn piece, and two paper clips. Fill cups ³/₄-full with warm water, and ask students to dissolve salt—a small amount will not dissolve. Ask students to tie paper clips to each end of their yarn, then place the ends inside the cups so the middle of the yarn hangs between. Have students lay the cardboard piece underneath the hanging yarn. Let models sit undisturbed for one week. Have students record daily observations in science journals and share results.

● What does your yarn look like after one week?
● What would happen if you left the yarn in the solution for another week?
● How is this experiment similar to the formation of stalactites and stalagmites in caves? How is it different?

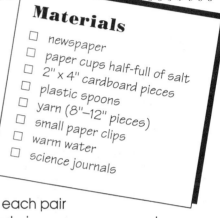

Conclusion

Students discover salt crystals forming along yarn pieces, accumulating in the center and dripping on the cardboard. This simulates the formation of stalagmites and stalactites in caves. The evaporation of water inside caves causes calcium carbonate crystals to form mineral columns on cave floors (stalagmites) and ceilings (stalactites). Extend learning by having students grow crystal columns in heat, cold, and high humidity.

Materials

- [ ] newspaper
- [ ] paper cups half-full of salt
- [ ] 2" x 4" cardboard pieces
- [ ] plastic spoons
- [ ] yarn (8"–12" pieces)
- [ ] small paper clips
- [ ] warm water
- [ ] science journals

Panning for Gold

Learning Outcome
Students learn how early miners collected gold.

Process Skills
▶ Students **investigate** ways to collect gold.

▶ Students **collect** buried "gold" using simulated panning and digging techniques.

▶ Students **communicate** their findings through discussion.

Connections
★ School
Discuss troubles and hardships gold miners experienced, such as travel, weather, housing, food prices, and homesickness. Ask students to imagine life as a gold miner and invite them to record their experiences in a "gold miner's journal."

★ Home
Invite family members to hide "gold" (pennies, wrapped candy, dried beans, colored beads) in or around their homes for students to find.

Exploration
In advance, hide "gold" in sand buckets—one bucket for every three or four students. Place tubs of water in a large, grassy area. Explain that gold is a valuable metallic mineral. Discuss past and present ways to collect and use gold. Take students to the "mining" area, and give each group a bucket of sand, spoons, and a cup. Have students dig in their buckets for five minutes using only their spoons, then place uncovered "gold nuggets" inside their cups. After digging is complete, demonstrate how miners panned for gold. Pour one cup of sand from the bucket into a pan, add water, then swirl the pan over a water tub, rinsing away sand to reveal "gold." Distribute cups and pie pans to students, and have them take turns panning for gold.

● Which mining method works better? Why?
● How does water help miners collect gold? What other methods could you use to collect gold?
● How would you collect gold buried in mountains or underground? What dangers might you encounter?

Materials
☐ heavy gravel or steel ball bearings spray-painted gold
☐ buckets of sand
☐ mining supplies (plastic spoons, cups, pie tins, large tubs of water)
☐ stopwatch

Conclusion
Students discover that panning is more efficient for collecting gold than digging, although more resources (pan, water) are required. Many early prospectors used pans, cradles, and troughs to collect gold deposits from riverbeds. Today, most "miners" use hydraulic drills and conveyors to collect and transport gold. Extend learning by discussing and investigating other metallic minerals.

Chip Mining

Learning Outcome

Students discover how mining can affect the land.

Process Skills

▶ Students **investigate** the pros and cons of mining.

▶ Students **observe** changes in cookies that have been "mined."

▶ Students **infer** how mining can affect the land.

Connections

★ *School*

Read aloud *Mama Is a Miner* by George Ella Lyon. Have students investigate different metals, gems, and fuel sources located underground.

★ Home

Have students and their families list ways to conserve fuels and other items made from rocks and minerals. Invite students to share their ideas with classmates.

Exploration

In advance, purchase or prepare cookies that include chocolate chips, nuts, and assorted candy pieces. Discuss mining with students—how it is done and the kinds of rocks, minerals, and natural resources collected. Distribute a cookie, toothpick, and paper towel to each student. Have students draw pictures of their cookies in science journals, including the number of "minerals" (food pieces) visible on the surface. Ask students to extract surface minerals using toothpicks only. Have them draw and record the number of minerals collected and the condition of their "mining site" after surface mining is complete. Ask students to mine the rest of their cookies, digging beneath the surface, then record additional minerals found.

● What kind and how many "minerals" did you find in your cookie?

● What did your mining site look like before mining? after "surface" mining? after "underground" mining?

● What are some advantages of mining? disadvantages?

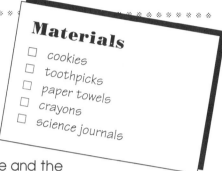

Materials

- ☐ cookies
- ☐ toothpicks
- ☐ paper towels
- ☐ crayons
- ☐ science journals

Conclusion

Although mining is a valuable tool for collecting valuable resources such as metals, gems, coal, and oil, there is a price to pay—mining depletes minerals in soil needed for plant growth, and destroys animal habitats. Students simulate the destruction of land as they collect "minerals"— cookies are moderately damaged by "mining" at the surface (strip mining) and extensively damaged digging beneath the surface (underground mining). Extend learning by inviting students to brainstorm alternative ways to collect and conserve natural resources.

Weather or Not

Learning Outcome

Students learn about the effects of weathering and acid rain on rocks.

Process Skills

▶ Students **experiment** with the effects of weathering using rock models.

▶ Students **observe** how abrasive actions (scraping) damage rock.

▶ Students **infer** how acid rain affects rock structures (e.g., statues, buildings, monuments).

Connections

★ School

Discuss the effects of weathering on statues, buildings, and other rock structures. Investigate the effects of weathering on ancient rock structures such as the pyramids of Egypt and Mexico, the stone statues on Easter Island, and the Great Wall of China.

★ Home

Invite students and their families to investigate the effects of weathering and erosion on their homes and play areas, or on statues and monuments in local parks and museums.

Exploration

Discuss weathering with students. Divide the class into partners and give each pair two pieces of chalk. Have students rub chalk pieces together over black paper, and record in science journals what happens to the chalk. Give each pair two more chalk pieces, labels, craft sticks, a cup of water, and a cup of vinegar. Ask students to label water cups *Rain* and vinegar cups *Acid Rain*. Have them place a piece of chalk into each cup, stir with craft sticks, and let soak for one hour. Ask students to draw pictures of their observations in science journals after five minutes, 30 minutes, and one hour. After time has elapsed, invite students to observe and feel the differences between chalk pieces.

● How is rubbing chalk pieces together similar to the effects of weathering on rocks? How is it different?
● How is chalk affected by "rain"? "acid rain"?
● How do you think rain affects rocks in our environment?

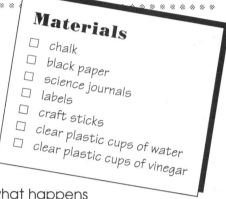

Materials
☐ chalk
☐ black paper
☐ science journals
☐ labels
☐ craft sticks
☐ clear plastic cups of water
☐ clear plastic cups of vinegar

Conclusion

Students discover that chalk pieces are damaged when rubbed together or exposed to acid (vinegar). These results simulate the effects of weathering (erosion) on rocks. Weathering is caused by chemicals in the environment or abrasive action from water, wind, and ice. Extend learning by investigating how water breaks down rock. Have students soak rocks overnight in coffee cans half-filled with water. The next day, invite students to shake covered cans for five to ten minutes, then uncover and observe the results.

Slip and Slide

Learning Outcome

Students learn how rocks are affected when layers of the earth shift and split apart during an earthquake.

Process Skills

▶ Students **construct models** of the earth's crust.

▶ Students use models to **observe** and **compare** how earthquakes affect the earth.

▶ Students **infer** that rocks split and break apart in earthquakes.

Connections

★ School

Discuss safety procedures for earthquakes and other natural disasters. Have students brainstorm supplies needed and actions to take during emergency situations.

★ Home

Have students and their families discuss proper safety procedures for earthquakes and other natural disasters at home. Encourage families to store emergency supplies and practice monthly drills in and around the home.

Exploration

Discuss how earth layers shift during earthquakes, causing rocks to split and break apart. Divide the class into groups of three or four and give each student two graham crackers. Distribute cake fillings, knives, and candy sprinkles to each group. Have students create earth models by carefully spreading alternating layers of filling between the graham crackers. Ask them to place candy sprinkles between layers to represent smaller rock pieces. Have students draw "before" diagrams of their models in science journals, identifying each layer. Invite students to slide or break apart graham crackers, then observe and record what happens to the inner layers.

● What happened to your "earth" layers when you slid or broke the crackers?
● What happened to your candy sprinkles when you split the layers? Did they stay in place or shift positions?
● What do you think happens to rock when layers shift during an earthquake?

Materials
- [ ] graham crackers
- [ ] paper plates
- [ ] cups of cake fillings (chocolate, raspberry, lemon, whipped cream)
- [ ] plastic knives
- [ ] candy sprinkles
- [ ] paper towels
- [ ] science journals

Conclusion

Students discover that layers shift and mix together as cracker pieces are pulled or broken apart. This simulates how earth layers shift during an earthquake. The earth's surface consists of several "plates" that move slowly past one another, squeezing and stretching rocks. If the force becomes too great, rocks rupture and shift, causing an earthquake. Extend learning by investigating faults—the central locations of earthquakes.

Creative Teaching Press, Inc.

Shake, Rattle, and Roll

Learning Outcome

Students learn how buildings withstand the impact of an earthquake.

Process Skills

▶ Students **investigate** the stability of model buildings during an earthquake simulation.

▶ Students **predict** how their structures will withstand the simulated earthquake.

▶ Students **communicate** their results through writing, drawing, and discussion.

Connections

★ **School**
Invite students to draw blueprints of earthquake-safe buildings. Have them explain how both people and property are protected. Invite students to share their creations with classmates.

★ **Home**
Invite students to take home earthquake trays and repeat the investigation with family members using other building materials such as gumdrops, apple pieces, and olives.

Exploration

In advance, build "earthquake trays" as shown below. Be certain rubber bands anchoring the cardboard to the box are taut but not over-stretched. To simulate an earthquake, pull one corner of the cardboard toward a corner of the box, then release. Give each group of students an earthquake tray. Ask groups to build earthquake-proof structures on their trays using toothpicks and miniature marshmallows. Have them construct buildings at least 30 cm high. When students have finished construction, ask them to simulate an earthquake to test the stability of their structures.

● Did your building withstand the "earthquake"?
● How can you improve your earthquake-proof building?
● How is the motion of the earthquake tray similar to a real earthquake?

Materials

☐ shallow cardboard boxes (canned good trays)
☐ small marbles (10–15 per box)
☐ flat cardboard (½" smaller than the inside dimensions of the box)
☐ small rubber bands
☐ stapler
☐ toothpicks
☐ miniature marshmallows
☐ rulers

Conclusion

Students discover that some of their structures withstand the motion of "earthquakes," while others fall apart. Engineers and architects try to design buildings that are sturdy, but also flexible enough to move and shift with earthquake movements. If they are not, buildings will collapse under the stress of the motion. Extend learning by inviting students to test shaped structures—triangular, square, rectangular—to determine which is most stable.

Real-Life Connections

As each science topic is studied, make real-life connections to professional, community, and family life:

▶ Invite a geologist to class to discuss career opportunities associated with geology.

▶ Invite a representative from a local mining company to discuss mining equipment and operations.

▶ Demonstrate to students how Geiger counters work, and discuss their applications.

▶ Invite a rock specialist to show students how rocks are polished.

▶ Invite a jeweler to discuss how various gems are cut or how jewelry is made. Create a birthday/birthstone chart.

Culminating Activity

Students can use their newly-acquired knowledge about rocks and minerals to turn the classroom or school gym into a rock museum for families and friends. Have students display rock and mineral collections (including identification cards for each sample). Samples can be displayed in egg crates or glued to index cards and placed in shirt gift boxes. Invite students to research and write reports on different gold rushes (California, Klondike, Colorado, Alaska) to complement a gold-panning demonstration. Have students include pictures with captions about famous miners. Display items and pictures that illustrate everyday uses of rocks and minerals.

Assessment

An important goal in early childhood science education is to generate curiosity and enthusiasm about science. In a hands-on program, students should receive credit for participation and involvement as well as comprehension.

Rubric

A rubric is a scoring guide that defines student performance. Use the Performance Evaluation and Rubric (page 31) to assess student progress for each exploration.

Portfolios

Student lab sheets, journals, and self-evaluations are important parts of science portfolios. All portfolio entries should be dated so they can be chronologically compared at any time. Teacher checklists and performance evaluations can also be helpful in keeping track of progress and achievements.

Anecdotal Records

Keep written records of observations that verify students' understanding of science concepts and processes during hands-on activities. Use these to assist in student and parent conferencing.

Student Conferences

Ask students to discuss their most interesting exploration. Guide them using questions such as: *What did you learn by doing this exploration? What might you do differently if you tried it again?*

Name _____ Date _____

My Science Work

Exploration:_____

My work was:

My best!   Good.   I can do better.

By doing this exploration, I learned _____

_____

_____

If I could do it again, I would _____

_____

Performance Evaluation

Student_____ Date _____

Check the level that best reflects student's performance.

Exploration:	Performance Level			
_____	Excellent	Very Good	Good	Needs Improvement
Shows motivation and curiosity for learning.				
Draws reasonable conclusions from science exploration.				
Demonstrates full understanding of concepts.				
Clearly communicates and listens to others.				
Accurately records and describes observations.				
Uses knowledge to solve problems or extend thinking.				
Comments:				

Rubric

Excellent
Goes beyond competency, adding creativity and insight to overall performance. Shows initiative and takes charge of learning. Listens attentively to others. Shows advanced critical thinking skills. Written work is polished with detailed explanations that extend into other subject areas.

Very Good
Uses skills effectively. Listens well during discussions, contributing thoughtful ideas and opinions. Work is neat and accurate, showing evidence of higher-level thinking. Does not take risks or extend ideas into other subject areas.

Good
Shows much effort and desire to learn but is still working on mastery of skills. Written work is accurate but shows little creativity or higher-level thinking. Follows directions well but needs extra encouragement and time to organize work.

Needs Improvement
Lacks organization and effort. Student is unsure of how to use materials or uses them incorrectly. Written work is inaccurate and shows little or no creativity. Does not follow directions and needs additional guidance to perform general tasks.

Bibliography

Children's Books

Barrett, Norman S. *Volcanoes.* (Picture Library) Franklin Watts, 1989.

Baylor, Byrd. *Everybody Needs a Rock.* Simon & Schuster Children's, 1985.

Baylor, Byrd. *If You Are a Hunter of Fossils.* Simon & Schuster Children's, 1984.

Chetwin, Grace. *Mr. Meredith and the Truly Remarkable Stone.* Bradbury Press, 1989.

Cole, Joanna. *The Magic School Bus Inside the Earth.* Scholastic Inc., 1989.

Harshman, Marc. *Rocks in My Pockets.* Dutton, 1991.

Jennings, Terry J. *Rocks.* Garret Educational Corporation, 1991.

Kimmel, Eric A. *Anansi and the Moss-Covered Rock.* Holiday House, 1988.

Lauber, Patricia. *Volcanoes and Earthquakes.* Scholastic Inc., 1991.

Lyon, George-Ella. *Mama Is a Miner.* Orchard, 1994.

Marcus, Elizabeth. *Rocks and Minerals.* Troll, 1983.

Steig, William. *Sylvester and the Magic Pebble.* Simon & Schuster Children's, 1987.

Resource Books

Cork, B. and M. Bramwell. *Rocks & Fossils.* (Hobby Guides Series) Random House, 1983.

Cvancara, Alan. *A Field Manual for the Amateur Geologist: Tools and Activities for Exploring Our Planet.* John Wiley and Sons, 1995.

Dixon, Dougal. *The Practical Geologist.* Simon & Schuster Trade, 1992.

Sorrell, Charles. *Rocks and Minerals.* (Golden Field Guide Series) Western Publishing Company Inc., 1973.

Symes, Dr. R.F. *Rocks & Minerals.* (Eyewitness Books) Alfred A. Knopf Inc., 1988.

Organizations

American Geological Institute
4220 King St.
Alexandria, VA 22302

National Earthquake Information Service
U.S. Geological Survey
Box 25046-MS 967
Denver Federal Center
Denver, CO 80225

U.S. Geological Survey
Geological Inquiries Group
907 National Center
Reston, VA 22092

Geological Equipment

Carolina Biological Supply Company
2700 York Rd.
Burlington, NC 27215

Ward's Natural Science Establishment, Inc.
5100 West Henrietta Rd,
P.O. Box 92912
Rochester, NY 14692

Earthquake Seismograph Charts

Superintendent of Documents
Government Printing Office
Washington, DC 20402

Creative Teaching Press, Inc.